Contents

What's in There?

What's in there?
  Gold and money.
Where's my share of it?
  The mouse ran away with it.
Where's the mouse?
  In her house.
Where's her house?
  In the wood.
Where's the wood?
  The fire burnt it.
Where's the fire?
  The water quenched it.

A Macmillan Poetry Picture Book

POP  Goes the WEASEL!

NONSENSE Rhymes

Illustrations by Anna Currey

MACMILLAN CHILDREN'S BOOKS

Acknowledgements

The publishers wish to thank the following for permission to use copyright material:

Carey Blyton, 'Bananas' from *Bananas in Pyjamas*, ABC Books, 1994, by permission of the Australian Broadcasting Corporation; **Charles Causley**, 'Charity Chadder' from *Collected Poems for Children*, Macmillan Children's Books, by permission of David Higham Associates on behalf of the author; **Sheree Fitch**, 'Doctor Stickles' from *Toes in My Nose*. Copyright © 1987 Sheree Fitch, by permission of Doubleday Canada Ltd; **Theresa Heine**, 'The Lonely Dragon' included in *Twinkle Twinkle, Chocolate Bar*, John Foster, ed., Oxford University Press, 1991, by permission of the author; **Doug MacLeod**, 'A Swamp Romp' from *The Garden of Bad Things*, by permission of Penguin Books Australia Ltd; **Spike Milligan**, 'Down the Stream the Swans All Glide', by permission of Spike Milligan Productions Ltd; **Alastair Reid**, 'Squishy Words (to be said when wet)' from *Ounce Dice Trice*, Abacus, 1991; **Irene Yates**, 'Danger', by permission of Laurence Pollinger Ltd on behalf of the author.

Every effort has been made to trace the copyright holders but if any have been inadvertently overlooked the publishers will be pleased to make the necessary arrangement at the first opportunity.

First published in 1999 by Macmillan Children's Books
A division of Macmillan Publishers Limited
25 Eccleston Place, London SW1W 9NF
Basingstoke and Oxford
Associated companies throughout the world.

ISBN 0 333 78075 2

Printed in Belgium

Where's the water?
  The brown bull drank it.
Where's the brown bull?
  At the back of Birnie's Hill.
Where's Birnie's Hill?
  All clad with snow.
Where's the snow?
  The sun melted it.
Where's the sun?
  High, high up in the air.

Anon.

5

Pop Goes the Weasel!

Up and down the City Road,
  In and out the Eagle,
That's the way the money goes,
  Pop goes the weasel!

A ha'penny for a cotton ball,
  A farthing for a needle,
That's the way the money goes,
  Pop goes the weasel!

Half a pound of tuppeny rice,
  Half a pound of treacle,
Mix it up and make it nice,
  Pop goes the weasel!

Anon.

Hey Diddle Diddle

Hey diddle diddle,
The cat and the fiddle,
The cow jumped over the moon;
The little dog laughed
To see such sport,
And the dish ran away
With the spoon.

Anon.

A Swamp Romp

Clomp Thump
Swamp Lump
Plodding in the Ooze,
Belly Shiver
Jelly Quiver
Squelching in my shoes.

Clomp Thump
Romp Jump
Mulching all the Mud,
Boot Trudge
Foot Sludge
Thud! Thud! Thud!

Doug MacLeod

Squishy Words

(to be said when wet)

SQUIFF
SQUIDGE
SQUAMOUS
SQUINNY
SQUELCH
SQUASH
SQUEEGEE
SQUIRT
SQUAB

Alastair Reid

Down the Stream
the Swans All Glide

Down the stream the swans all glide;
It's quite the cheapest way to ride.
Their legs get wet,
Their tummies wetter:
I think after all
The bus is better.

Spike Milligan

The Grand Old Duke of York

Oh, the grand old Duke of York,
   He had ten thousand men,
He marched them up to the top of the hill,
   And he marched them down again.

And when they were up they were up,
   And when they were down they were down,
And when they were only half way up,
   They were neither up nor down.

Anon.

Peter Piper

Peter Piper picked a peck of
   pickled pepper;
Did Peter Piper pick a peck of
   pickled pepper?
If Peter Piper picked a peck of
   pickled pepper,
Where's the peck of pickled pepper
Peter Piper picked?

Anon.

Down the Slippery Slide

Down the slippery slide they slid
Sitting slightly sideways;
Slipping swiftly see them skid
On holidays and Fridays.

Anon.

Betty Botter

Betty Botter bought some butter,
But, she said, this butter's bitter;
If I put it in my batter,
It will make my batter bitter,
But a bit of better butter
Will make my batter better.
So she bought a bit of butter
Better than her bitter butter,
And she put it in her batter,
And it made her batter better,
So 'twas better Betty Botter
Bought a bit of better butter.

Anon.

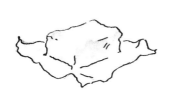  

Nobody Loves Me

Nobody loves me,
Everybody hates me,
I think I'll go and eat worms.

Big fat squishy ones,
Little thin skinny ones,
See how they wriggle and squirm.

Bite their heads off.
"Schlurp!" they're lovely,
Throw their tails away.

Nobody knows
How big I grows
on worms three times a day.

Anon.

Wish I was a Little Grub

Wish I was a little grub
with whiskers round my tummy.
I'd climb into a honey-pot
and make my tummy gummy.

Anon.

Three Little Ghostesses

Three little ghostesses,
Sitting on postesses,
Eating buttered toastesses,
Greasing their fistesses,
Up to the wristesses,
Oh, what beastesses
To make such feastesses!

Anon.

The Dark Wood

In the dark, dark wood,
  there was a dark, dark house,
And in that dark, dark house,
  there was a dark, dark room,
And in that dark, dark room,
  there was a dark, dark cupboard,
And in that dark, dark cupboard,
  there was a dark, dark shelf,
And on that dark, dark shelf,
  there was a dark, dark box,
And in that dark, dark box
  there was a GHOST!

Anon.

Danger

Large red dragons
Are dangerous.
But small, pretty
Pink ones are usually
Only
Pretending.

Irene Yates

The Lonely Dragon

A dragon is sad
Because everyone thinks
A dragon is fierce and brave,
And roars out flames,
And eats everybody,
Whoever comes near his cave.
But a dragon likes people,
A dragon needs friends,
A dragon is lonely and sad,
If anyone knows
Of a friend for a dragon,
A dragon would be very glad.

Theresa Heine

Anna Maria

Anna Maria she sat on the fire;
The fire was too hot,
 she sat on the pot;
The pot was too round,
 she sat on the ground;
The ground was too flat,
 she sat on the cat;
The cat ran away with Maria on her back.

Anon.

Tickly, Tickly

Tickly, tickly, on your knee,
If you laugh you don't love me.

Anon.

Doctor Stickles

Dr Stickles tickled me
And I began to giggle.
Dr Stickles tickled harder
Then I began to wiggle.
When Dr Stickles tickled my toes
I laughed and so would you.
Then I tickled Dr Stickles
Because he was ticklish, too!

Sheree Fitch

Bananas

Bananas,
In pyjamas,
Are coming down the stairs;
Bananas,
In pyjamas,
Are coming down in pairs;
Bananas,
In pyjamas,
Are chasing teddy bears—
'Cos on Tuesdays
They all try to
CATCH THEM UNAWARES

Carey Blyton

22

There was a Crooked Man

There was a crooked man,
   And he walked a crooked mile,
He found a crooked sixpence
   Against a crooked stile;
He bought a crooked cat,
   Which caught a crooked mouse,
And they all lived together
   In a little crooked house.

Anon.

Charity Chadder

Charity Chadder
Borrowed a ladder,
Leaned it against the moon,
Climbed to the top
Without a stop
On the 31st of June,
Brought down every single star,
Kept them all in a pickle jar.

Charles Causley

Mrs Mason Bought a Basin

Mrs Mason bought a basin.
Mrs Tyson said, "What a nice 'un."
"What did it cost?" said Mrs Frost.
"Half a crown," said Mrs Brown.
"Did it indeed!" said Mrs Reed.
"It did for certain," said Mrs Burton.
   Then Mrs Nix, up to her tricks,
   Threw the basin on the bricks.

Anon.

Rub-a-Dub-Dub

Rub-a-dub-dub,
Three men in a tub,
And who do you think they be?
The butcher, the baker,
The candlestick-maker,
Turn 'em out, knaves all three.

Anon.

Tweedledum and Tweedledee

Tweedledum and Tweedledee
   Agreed to have a battle,
For Tweedledum said Tweedledee
   Had spoiled his nice new rattle.
Just then flew by a monstrous crow,
   As big as a tar-barrel,
Which frightened both the heroes so,
   They quite forgot their quarrel.

Anon.

Kittens with Mittens

Where are you going,
My little kittens?

We are going to town
To get us some mittens.

What! mittens for kittens!
Do kittens wear mittens?
Who ever saw little kittens with mittens?

Anon.

A Hat for a Cat

Where are you going,
My little cat?

I am going to town,
To get me a hat.

What! a hat for a cat!
A cat get a hat!
Who ever saw a cat with a hat?

Anon.

The Man in the Moon

The man in the moon
Came down too soon,
And asked his way to Norwich;
He went by the south,
And burnt his mouth
With supping cold plum porridge.

Anon.

There was an Old Woman Tossed Up in a Basket

There was an old woman tossed up
  in a basket,
   Seventeen times as high as the moon;
And where she was going, I couldn't
  but ask it,
   For in her hand she carried a broom.
Old woman, old woman, old woman,
  quoth I,
   O whither, O whither, O whither so high?
To sweep the cobwebs off the sky!
   Shall I go with you? Aye, by-and-by.

Anon.